**Core Knowledge Language Arts®**

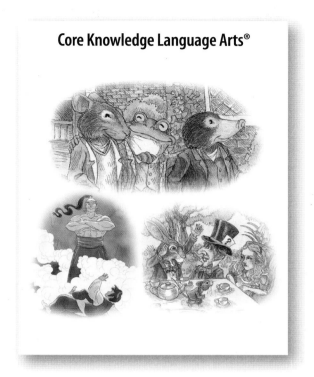

# Classic Tales
## Unit 1 Reader

### Skills Strand
### GRADE 3

Amplify learning.

Core Knowledge®

# Table of Contents
# Classic Tales
## Unit 1 Reader

# Where in the World Do These Tales Come From?

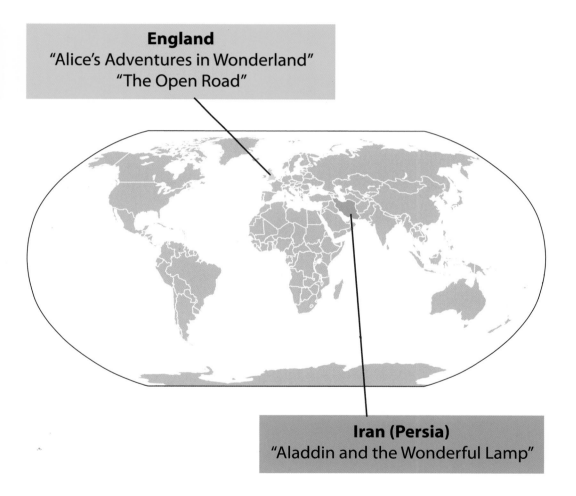

**England**
"Alice's Adventures in Wonderland"
"The Open Road"

**Iran (Persia)**
"Aladdin and the Wonderful Lamp"

# Chapter 1
# Aladdin and the Wonderful Lamp, Part I

There once was a poor boy whose name was Aladdin. His father was a tailor. When his father died, Aladdin's mother had to work to earn a living.

One day, a stranger greeted Aladdin.

"Tell me, son," said the stranger. "Are you the son of the tailor?"

"Yes," said Aladdin.

The stranger threw his arms around him. "My dear nephew!" he cried. "Your father was my brother! Now I learn he is dead! What a shame!"

*A stranger greeted Aladdin.*

Aladdin took the man to his mother. She was surprised. Her husband had never spoken of a brother. Even so, she greeted the man kindly. When he promised to help Aladdin become a merchant, she believed him.

But the stranger was not Aladdin's uncle. He was a magician from faraway north Africa. He had come to Persia in search of a magic lamp. It was said that this lamp would make a man rich. To find the lamp, the magician needed a helper. He was looking for someone who would help without asking any questions. He thought Aladdin was just the right person.

The next day, the magician came to get Aladdin.

"Come with me," he said. "I will introduce you to other merchants." Then, he led the boy out into the country.

*Aladdin took the man to meet his mother.*

The magician led Aladdin up a steep mountain. They climbed for an hour. Then, they came to a spot where no flowers grew.

"Get some sticks," said the magician. "We will make a fire. Then, I will show you something amazing."

Aladdin did as he was told. The magician lit the fire. Then, he threw perfumes into it and chanted magical words. The sky darkened. Thunder rumbled. The earth opened at their feet. There before them was a large stone with a brass ring attached.

"Under this stone is a treasure," said the magician. "It will make you richer than any king. Lift the stone by the ring. Then, go down the stairs. You will pass many treasures, but you must not touch them. You will enter a garden. There you will see a lamp hanging from a tree. Bring that lamp to me. Once you have it, you may gather any of the treasures that you see."

Aladdin was amazed. He could not believe what he was being asked to do. But he agreed.

"Take this ring," said the magician. "It will keep you safe from harm." Aladdin took it and placed it on his finger.

*The magician told Aladdin what to do.*

Aladdin lifted the stone. He went down the stairs. He made his way through a hallway of treasures. He was careful not to touch anything. When he found the lamp, he tucked it inside his bag. Then, he filled his pockets with all the glittering things he saw. He didn't know they were precious gems. He was thinking, "I will gather these pretty things to play with at home."

All those gems weighed Aladdin down. When he came to the top of the staircase, he could not climb out. "Give me a hand, Uncle," he cried.

"First, give me the lamp," the magician answered.

The lamp was buried in the bag Aladdin was carrying.

"I cannot reach it now," Aladdin said.

"Hand it up to me," said the magician.

"But I can't!" Aladdin said.

The magician grew angry. "The lamp!" he cried, for that was all he cared about.

But Aladdin did not want to drop anything. "I will give it to you when I get out," he said.

The impatient magician felt he could wait no longer. He chanted a magic spell. The stone rolled back, trapping Aladdin in the black darkness of the cave.

*"Give me the lamp," said the magician.*

# Chapter 2
# Aladdin and the Wonderful Lamp, Part II

Aladdin was trapped in the cave.

"Uncle!" he called. "Help me!" But there was no reply. The magician had whisked himself back to north Africa. All he wanted was the lamp. If Aladdin would not help him get that, he cared nothing for Aladdin.

For three days, Aladdin stayed in the pitch-black cave. At first, he shouted. Then, he wept. Finally, he put his hands together to pray. As he did so, he happened to rub the ring that the magician had placed on his finger. A genie rose before him.

"What is your wish?" said the genie of the ring.

Aladdin was scared but he managed to say, "Take me out of this cave!"

Poof!

Aladdin found himself outside again.

*A genie rose before Aladdin.*

He ran home to tell his mother all that had happened. He showed her the gems, which she thought were just pretty things as well. Then, he showed her the lamp.

"It is so dirty," said Aladdin's mother. "Let me clean it. Then, perhaps I can sell it and get us some food."

She took a cloth and started rubbing the lamp. Suddenly, a monstrous genie appeared. This genie was far bigger than the one that had appeared to Aladdin before.

"What is your wish?" thundered the genie of the lamp.

The poor woman almost fainted with fear. Aladdin said, "We are hungry! Get us something to eat!"

Poof!

The genie returned with twelve gold platters piled high with food. Aladdin and his mother ate their fill. Then, they sold the silver platters and bought more food.

*The genie returned with platters of food.*

One day at the market, Aladdin caught a glimpse of the Sultan's daughter. She was so beautiful that he fell in love at once. He told his mother that he wanted to marry the princess.

Aladdin's mother laughed. "Have you lost your senses?" she said. "Your father was a poor tailor!"

"Remember the glittering things from the cave?" said Aladdin. "Take them and offer them as a gift to the Sultan."

Aladdin's mother went to the Sultan. "My lord," she said. "My son Aladdin wishes to marry your daughter."

The Sultan burst out laughing. "Your son and my daughter?" he boomed. "Ha!"

Aladdin's mother opened her cloth and displayed the gems.

The Sultan fell silent. He stepped forward to look closely at what he saw. He realized that they were not just pretty, glittering things.

"These are astounding!" the Sultan thought. "I have never seen such radiant gems!"

The Sultan spoke again: "Your son may marry my daughter—on one condition. He must send forty servants, each carrying a bowl of gems like these."

*Aladdin's mother showed the Sultan the glittering things from the cave.*

When Aladdin heard this, he rubbed his lamp. The genie appeared. Aladdin repeated the Sultan's wish. Almost instantly, the genie returned with forty servants. Each servant carried a large golden bowl. Half of the bowls were filled with pearls and diamonds; the others were filled with rubies and emeralds.

The Sultan was amazed. He agreed that Aladdin could marry his daughter.

*The genie returned with forty servants.*

Aladdin was delighted. He rubbed the lamp. The genie appeared.

Aladdin commanded the genie to prepare a wedding fit for a prince. The forty servants appeared again. They brought Aladdin rich clothes and sweet perfumes. They gave him a beautiful horse, which he rode to the wedding. They threw gold pieces to the people who lined the streets to see him. They made Aladdin a palace right next to the Sultan's palace. They even rolled out a thick, red carpet for the princess; it stretched from the Sultan's home to Aladdin's palace. When the Sultan saw Aladdin's palace, he was sure that Aladdin was the right husband for his daughter. They celebrated their wedding with a feast and music. The party lasted all day and all night.

*Aladdin married the Sultan's daughter.*

# Chapter 3

# Aladdin and the Wonderful Lamp, Part III

Aladdin was delighted with his new life. He felt that everything was perfect. But danger lurked.

The magician heard of Aladdin's good fortune. "That lazy boy?" he said. "Married to the Sultan's daughter? Surely this must be the magic of the lamp."

He whisked himself back to Persia. He dressed as a poor peddler and carried a few shiny lamps in a basket. As he walked by Aladdin's palace, he shouted, "New lamps for old!"

Aladdin was out hunting. His wife, the princess, heard the voice from the street.

"We have that ugly, old lamp," she thought. "I would gladly trade it for a shiny, new one."

She handed Aladdin's lamp to the magician. He handed her a new lamp.

*The princess traded the old lamp for a shiny, new one.*

The magician hurried away and later that day, he rubbed the lamp. The genie appeared.

"Take Aladdin's palace and all that it contains," commanded the magician. "Set it down in my home of north Africa."

"I hear and I obey," said the genie of the lamp.

*The magician rubbed the lamp.*

The next morning, the Sultan looked out the window. His daughter's palace was gone. So was the princess. He sent his soldiers out and they dragged Aladdin before the Sultan.

"Find my daughter!" he stormed. "If you fail, you die!"

*The Sultan sent his soldiers to get Aladdin.*

Poor Aladdin wandered far from the city. He walked beside a river and rubbed his hands, wondering what to do.

The genie of the ring appeared once more.

"What do you wish?" asked the genie of the ring.

"Bring my palace and my beloved wife home to me," begged Aladdin.

"Sadly," said the genie, "I cannot. That duty belongs only to the genie of the lamp."

"Then, take me to be with my wife."

Poof!

Aladdin found himself in Africa. His wife greeted him joyfully. She told him about the peddler and the lamp. When Aladdin heard this, he knew that the magician had used the lamp to work his evil deed. He and his wife made a plan to get the lamp back.

*Aladdin begged the genie for help.*

The next day, the princess cooked the magician a fine supper. Aladdin kept out of sight. She slipped poison into the magician's cup. One sip was all it took. The magician fell on the floor, dead.

Aladdin ran in and found the lamp. The magician had hidden it in his sleeve. Aladdin rubbed the lamp. The monstrous genie appeared.

"What do you wish?" the genie of the lamp thundered.

"Take this palace, with all it contains," commanded Aladdin. "Carry it to Persia and set it down beside the Sultan's home."

*Aladdin told the genie his wish.*

"I hear and I obey," replied the genie of the lamp.

The palace was lifted up into the air.

The next morning, the Sultan arose and looked out the window. He was very happy to see his daughter and her palace once again. He ordered a month of celebrations.

From then on, Aladdin lived with the princess in peace, pleasure, and safety. When the old Sultan died, Aladdin took his throne. He ruled justly over all people, rich and poor.

*The Sultan awoke to see his daughter.*

# Chapter 4

# Alice's Adventures in Wonderland, Part I

*In 1865, the English author Lewis Carroll introduced the world to a girl named Alice and the strange and funny world of Wonderland.*

Alice was beginning to get very tired of sitting by her sister on the bank of the river with nothing to do. Once or twice, she had peeked into the book her sister was reading. But the book had no pictures or conversations in it.

"What is the use of a book," thought Alice, "without pictures or conversations?"

It was a hot day. The heat made Alice feel sleepy. She was thinking if the pleasure of making a daisy-chain would be worth the trouble of getting up and picking the daisies. Just then, a White Rabbit ran past her.

*Alice sees the White Rabbit.*

There was nothing so very remarkable in that; nor did Alice think it so very peculiar to hear the Rabbit say to itself, "Oh dear! Oh dear! I shall be too late!" But when the Rabbit took a watch out of its pocket, Alice jumped to her feet. She ran after the Rabbit and saw him pop down a large rabbit hole.

Alice followed the Rabbit down the hole, never once thinking how she would get out again. The rabbit hole dipped suddenly down. Alice found herself falling down what seemed to be a very deep well.

*Alice followed the Rabbit.*

Either the well was very deep, or she fell very slowly, for she had plenty of time to look about her. She looked at the sides of the well. They were filled with cupboards and bookshelves.

"Well!" thought Alice to herself. "After a fall like this, I shall think nothing of tumbling down the stairs!"

Down, down, down. Would the fall ever come to an end?

"I wonder how many miles I've fallen by this time." Alice said aloud. "I must be getting somewhere near the center of the earth. Let me see: that would be four thousand miles down, I think. I wonder if I shall fall right through the earth! How funny it will be to come out among the people that walk with their heads pointing downwards! I shall have to ask them what the name of the country is. 'Please, Ma'am, is this New Zealand? Or Australia?'" She felt that she was dozing off when suddenly, thump! Down she came upon a heap of sticks and dry leaves.

*Alice fell down, down, down.*

Alice was not hurt. She got up and looked around. Before her was a long tunnel. The White Rabbit was hurrying down it. Alice ran after him. She heard him say, "Oh my ears and whiskers, how late it's getting!" She thought she was catching up to the White Rabbit. Then, she turned the corner and, poof! He was gone.

Alice found herself in a long, low hall. There were many doors, but they were all locked. She wondered how she would ever get out.

Suddenly, she came upon a little three-legged table. It was made of solid glass. There was nothing on it but a tiny, golden key. But, it would not open any of the doors.

*Alice ran after the White Rabbit.*

Then, Alice spotted a curtain she had not noticed before. Behind it was a little door about fifteen inches high. She tried the little, golden key in the lock. It fit!

The door led into a small tunnel. It was not much larger than a rat hole. Alice knelt down and looked out into the loveliest garden she had ever seen. She longed to get out of that dark hall. She longed to wander about the garden. But the doorway was tiny. She could not even get her head through it.

There seemed to be no use in waiting by the little door so Alice went back to the table. This time, she found a little bottle on it.

"Hmm," said Alice. "That was not there before."

Alice looked closely at the bottle. The label said, 'DRINK ME.'

"I'll look first," Alice said, "to see if it's marked Poison."

The bottle was not marked Poison so Alice decided to taste it. She found it had a sort of mixed flavor. It tasted like cherry tart, custard, pineapple, roast turkey, toffee, and hot buttered toast. Alice drank it up.

*Alice tasted what was in the bottle.*

# Alice's Adventures in Wonderland, Part II

*When last we saw Alice, she had decided to drink from a little bottle. The contents of the bottle tasted rather odd.*

"What a curious feeling!" said Alice. She was shrinking smaller and smaller. Soon, she was only ten inches high. That was just the right size to fit through the little door that led to the garden. But, when she got to the door, she found she had forgotten the little, golden key. She went back to the table for it, but she was too short to reach it.

Alice sat down and cried, but soon her eye fell on a little, glass box that was under the table. She opened it and found a very small cake. The words 'EAT ME' were spelled out on the cake with currants.

"I'll eat it," said Alice enthusiastically.

*Alice found a small cake.*

"Curiouser and curiouser!" cried Alice. "Now, I'm growing larger and larger! Goodbye, feet!"

Alice's head bumped against the roof of the hall. She was nine feet tall. She grabbed the little, golden key and ran to the garden door.

But, she was now too large to go through the doorway! All she could do was peek into the garden with one eye.

*Alice grabbed the key.*

Alice sat down and began to cry again. She went on, crying gallons of tears, until there was a large pool around her.

Then, Alice heard a pattering of feet in the distance. It was the White Rabbit returning. He was splendidly dressed, with a pair of white gloves in one hand and a large fan in the other. He was muttering to himself, "Oh, The Duchess! Won't she be cross if I've kept her waiting!"

When the Rabbit came near her, Alice tried to speak to him.

"If you please, sir—"

The Rabbit was startled. He dropped his gloves and his fan and scurried away into the darkness.

"How odd everything is today!" said Alice.

*Alice saw the White Rabbit again.*

As she said this, Alice could see that she was shrinking again. In another moment, splash! She was up to her chin in water. Poor Alice was swimming in a pool of her own tears.

"I wish I hadn't cried so much!" said Alice as she swam about in search of a way out. Thankfully, Alice did find a way out. She was not one for sitting still doing nothing, so she began to wander further and further into Wonderland.

*Alice swam in a pool of her own tears.*

It was at that point that she came upon a large, blue Caterpillar. The Caterpillar was sitting on a mushroom and smoking a pipe.

Alice stood on her tiptoes and peeked over the edge of the mushroom. Her eyes met those of the Caterpillar. The two of them looked at each other for some time in silence. At last, the Caterpillar took the pipe out of its mouth and asked, "Who are you?"

Alice replied, "I—I hardly know, sir. I know who I was when I got up this morning, but I have been changed several times since then."

"What do you mean by that?" said the Caterpillar sternly. "Explain yourself!"

"I can't explain myself, sir," said Alice, "because I'm not myself, you see."

"I don't see," said the Caterpillar.

"I'm afraid I can't put it more clearly," Alice replied. "I find that being so many different sizes in one day is very confusing."

"It isn't," said the Caterpillar.

*Alice came upon the Caterpillar.*

Alice felt a little irritated by the Caterpillar and she turned away.

"Come back!" the Caterpillar called. "I've something important to say!"

This sounded promising, so Alice turned and came back again.

"Keep your temper," said the Caterpillar.

"Is that all?" said Alice.

In a minute or two, the Caterpillar took the pipe out of his mouth and got down off the mushroom. Then, he crawled away into the grass. As he went, he said, "One side will make you grow taller. The other side will make you grow shorter."

"One side of what?" thought Alice to herself.

"Of the mushroom," said the Caterpillar.

In another moment, the Caterpillar was gone.

Alice broke off a bit of each side of the mushroom. She ate small bites and managed to bring herself back to her normal height.

*Alice watched the Caterpillar crawl away.*

# Alice's Adventures in Wonderland, Part III

*Next, Alice wandered until she came upon a Cheshire Cat. The Cat was sitting on the branch of a tree and grinning from ear to ear. Alice was beginning to wish her time in Wonderland would come to an end.*

"Cheshire Cat," Alice said, "would you tell me, please, which way I should walk from here?"

"That depends a lot on where you want to get to," said the Cat.

"I don't care much where—" said Alice.

"Then it doesn't matter which way you go," said the Cat.

"—so long as I get somewhere," Alice added.

"Oh, you're sure to do that," said the Cat, "if you only walk long enough."

Alice tried another question, "What sort of people live here?"

*Alice came upon the Cheshire Cat.*

"In that direction," said the Cat, waving his right paw, "lives a Mad Hatter. In that direction lives a March Hare. Visit either of them if you like: they're both mad."

"But I don't want to visit with mad people," Alice remarked.

"Oh, you can't help that," said the Cat. "We're all mad here."

Then, the Cat vanished slowly, beginning at the end of his tail and ending with his grin, which remained some time after the rest of him had gone.

"Well!" thought Alice. "A grin without a cat! How curious!"

*Alice spoke with the Cheshire Cat.*

She walked a bit and came to a house with a table set up in front. The March Hare and the Mad Hatter were having tea. A Dormouse was sitting between them. The table was large but the three of them were all crowded together at one corner of it.

"No room! No room!" they cried out when they saw Alice coming.

"There's plenty of room!" said Alice indignantly. She sat down in a large armchair at one end of the table.

"Have some lemonade," said the March Hare.

Alice looked all around the table.

"I don't see any lemonade," she remarked.

"There isn't any," said the March Hare.

"Then, it wasn't very civil of you to offer it," said Alice angrily.

"It wasn't very civil of you to sit down without being invited," said the March Hare.

*Alice met the March Hare, the Mad Hatter, and the Dormouse.*

The Mad Hatter looked at Alice for some time. At last, he said, "Why is a raven like a writing desk?"

"A riddle!" thought Alice. "We shall have some fun now!"

"I believe I can guess that," she added aloud.

"Do you mean that you think you know the answer to it?" asked the March Hare.

"Exactly so," said Alice.

"Then, you should say what you mean," the March Hare went on.

"I do," Alice replied. "At least, I mean what I say— that's the same thing, you know."

"Not the same thing at all!" said the Mad Hatter. "Why, you might as well say that 'I see what I eat' is the same thing as 'I eat what I see!'"

"You might as well say," added the Dormouse, which seemed to be walking and talking in its sleep, "that 'I breathe when I sleep' is the same thing as 'I sleep when I breathe!'"

*The March Hare answered Alice.*

"It is the same thing with you," said the Mad Hatter. Then, he turned to Alice again and asked, "Have you guessed the riddle yet?"

"No, I give up," Alice replied. "What's the answer?"

"I haven't the slightest idea," said the Mad Hatter.

"Nor I," said the March Hare.

"Well," thought Alice, "this is the strangest tea party I ever was at in all my life!"

Alice stayed for a while longer and listened to the Dormouse tell a story about three sisters who lived at the bottom of a treacle well. The story was very odd indeed. Alice, confused by the tale, frequently questioned the Dormouse. At last, a frustrated Alice walked off.

"It's the strangest tea party I ever was at in all my life!" Alice concluded.

*Alice walked away frustrated.*

# Alice's Adventures in Wonderland, Part IV

# Chapter 7

*In this final chapter, Alice comes across even more odd things in Wonderland.*

As Alice wandered further into Wonderland, she found a door in a tree that led into a hallway. The hallway led into the beautiful garden that she had been in earlier. Remarkably, upon entering the garden, she met a huge number of people, including royal courtiers and royal children, as well as the King and Queen of Hearts. They were about to begin a game of croquet and they invited Alice to play.

The game itself proved to be nothing but chaos, partly because the croquet ground was all ridges and furrows. The croquet balls were live hedgehogs and the mallets were flamingos. Alice found that her biggest problem was managing her flamingo and stopping the balls—or hedgehogs—from walking away. In addition, the players all played at the same time without waiting for their turn. The Queen, for her part, began stamping about and shouting, "Off with his head!" or "Off with her head!"

*Alice came across even more odd things in Wonderland.*

But lucky for Alice, she was removed from the game by none other than the Queen who was eager for Alice to meet the Mock Turtle. On their way to meet the Mock Turtle, Alice was introduced to the Gryphon. What are a Mock Turtle and a Gryphon? Alice did not know either; nor did she ever get an answer that made sense. The best answer is that they are two more examples of the extraordinary inhabitants of Wonderland.

Together the Mock Turtle and the Gryphon told the Queen and Alice stories of their school days. They recalled the subjects they had studied in school, including Reeling, Writhing, and Ambition, not to mention ancient and modern Mystery. Alice was quite certain that she had not yet studied these subjects.

*Alice met the Mock Turtle and the Gryphon.*

This odd conversation was stopped by the news that an important trial had begun. Alice raced off with the Gryphon to discover that the Knave of Hearts was on trial for stealing some tarts.

Just like the game of croquet, the trial itself was a confusing mess. The witnesses were not at all helpful. Quite strangely, Alice herself was called as a witness. When the Queen said that the sentence should be announced before the jury had decided upon their verdict, Alice was ready to scream. In fact, she did.

"Stuff and nonsense!" said Alice loudly. "The idea of having the sentence first!"

"Hold your tongue!" said the Queen, turning purple.

"I won't!" said Alice.

"Off with her head!" yelled the Queen.

*Alice spoke at the trial.*

Again, lucky for Alice, just at that moment she woke up on the river bank beside her sister. The sun was still shining and it was indeed a beautiful day. Alice eagerly told her sister all about her dream and her adventures in Wonderland. Alice's sister was quite entertained by the stories of Wonderland and the way in which Alice told them. Alice's eyes twinkled and shone as she told her sister about the Caterpillar, the Cheshire Cat, the Mad Hatter, the March Hare, the King and Queen of Hearts, not to mention the White Rabbit.

As Alice skipped away to enjoy some afternoon tea, her sister imagined this magical world full of curious creatures. Alice's sister hoped that Alice would always remember the day that she dreamed of Wonderland and continue to tell the stories.

*Alice told her sister of her adventures.*

# Chapter 8 The Open Road, Part I

*In 1908, the Scottish author Kenneth Grahame delighted readers with stories of Toad, Mole, and Rat and their adventures in a book called "The Wind in the Willows."*

"Won't you take me to call on Toad?" said Mole to his friend, Rat. "I've heard so much about him."

"Why, of course," said Rat. "Get the boat out and we'll paddle up there at once. It's never the wrong time to call on Toad. Early or late, he's always the same fellow: always good-tempered, always glad to see you, and always sorry when you go!"

"He must be a very nice animal," said Mole, as he got into the boat.

"He is indeed the best of animals," replied Rat, "so simple, and so friendly. Perhaps he's not very clever—we can't all be smart. It may be that he is both boastful and conceited. But Toady is a great friend."

*Rat told Mole about his friend, Toad.*

Rounding a bend in the river, they came in sight of a handsome, dignified old house. It was faded red brick, with well-kept lawns reaching down to the water's edge.

"There's Toad Hall," said Rat. "See that creek on the left? That leads to Toad's boathouse. That's where we'll leave the boat. The stables are over there. That's the banquet hall you're looking at now—very old, that is. Toad is rather rich, you know. This is really one of the nicest houses around, though we never admit as much to Toad."

They glided up the creek and passed into the shadow of a large boathouse. There they saw many large boats. Some were slung from the cross beams. Some were hauled up on a slip. But none of them were in the water. The place seemed deserted.

Rat looked around him. "I see how it is," he said. "Boating is old news. Toad is tired of it and done with it. I wonder what new fad he has taken up now. Come along and let's go see. We shall hear all about it soon enough."

*Rat and Mole arrived at Toad Hall.*

They stepped out of the boat and walked across the flower-decked lawn. They found Toad resting in a wicker garden chair. He had large map spread out on his knees.

"Hooray!" he cried, jumping up upon seeing them. "This is splendid!" He shook the paws of both of them warmly, never waiting for an introduction to Mole. "How kind of you!" he went on, dancing round them. "I was just going to send a boat down the river for you, Ratty, with strict orders that you were to come here at once, whatever you were doing. You don't know how lucky it is, your turning up just now!"

"What a delightful house you have!" said Mole.

"Finest house on the whole river," cried Toad proudly. "Or anywhere else, for that matter," he could not help adding.

*Rat and Mole found Toad looking at a map.*

# Chapter 9
# The Open Road,
## Part II

*Toad was so excited that Rat and Mole had come for a visit.*

"Now then," Toad said. "You fellows must help me. It's most important!"

"You want us to help you with your boating?" asked Rat.

"O, pooh, boating!" said Toad, in great disgust. "A silly, boyish amusement. I gave that up long ago. A waste of time, that's what it is. It makes me very sorry to see you fellows, who ought to know better, spending all your time thinking about boating. No, I've discovered the real thing, the best occupation for a lifetime. I plan to spend the rest of my life on it, and can only wish I hadn't spent so many years boating. Come with me, dear Ratty, and your dear friend also. Come with me just as far as the stable yard, and you shall see what you shall see!"

*Toad led Rat and Mole to the stable yard.*

Toad led the way to the stable yard. Rat followed, with a most unhappy look on his face. There, for all to see was a travel wagon, shining with newness. It was painted yellow and green.

"There you are!" cried Toad. "There's real life for you in that travel wagon. The open road! The dusty highway! Camps, villages, towns, cities! Here today, up and off to somewhere else tomorrow! Travel, new places to see, fun! The whole world before you! A horizon that's always changing! Mind you: this is the very finest wagon of its sort that was ever made. Come and look at the inside. Planned all of it myself, I did!'

Mole followed Toad eagerly up the steps and into the wagon. Rat did not move. He only snorted and put his hands deep into his pockets.

*"There you are!" cried Toad.*

The wagon had little sleeping bunks and a table that folded up against the wall. It had a cooking stove, lockers, and bookshelves. It had a birdcage with a bird in it. It had pots, pans, jugs, and kettles of every size.

"All complete!" said Toad happily. "You'll find that nothing whatever has been forgotten, when we make our start this afternoon."

"I beg your pardon," said Rat. "But did I hear you say something about 'WE', and 'STARTING' and 'THIS AFTERNOON'?"

"Yes, yes!" begged Toad. "You've GOT to come. I can't possibly go without you. So please don't argue—it's the one thing I can't stand. You surely don't mean to stick to your dull, old river all your life and just live in a hole in a bank and go boating? I want to show you the world!"

"I don't care," said Rat, doggedly. "I'm not coming and that's that. I am going to stick to my old river and live in a hole and go boating, as I've always done. What's more, Mole's going to stick with me and do as I do. Aren't you, Mole?"

*Toad, Mole, and Rat inside the travel wagon.*

"Of course I am," said Mole, loyally.

"I'll always stick with you, Rat. What you say has got to be. All the same, it sounds as if it might have been, well, rather fun, you know!" he added, wistfully.

Poor Mole! The Life Adventurous was a new thing to him and so thrilling. It was all so tempting. He had fallen in love at first sight with the yellow-colored wagon.

Rat saw what was passing in Mole's mind and began to change his mind. He hated disappointing people and he very much liked Mole.

Toad was watching both of them closely.

"Come in and have some lunch," he said. "We'll talk it over. We don't need to decide anything in a hurry. Of course, I don't really care. I only want you fellows to have fun. Live for others! That's my motto in life."

*Toad leads Mole and Rat back to Toad Hall.*

# Chapter 10
## The Open Road, Part III

Lunch was wonderful, as everything at Toad Hall always was. During the meal, Toad spoke to Mole. He played inexperienced Mole like one would play a harp. He described what would happen on a trip and the joys of the open road in a glowing way. Mole could hardly sit still in his chair because he was so excited.

In the end, Rat allowed Toad and Mole to change his mind. He could not disappoint his friends. So after lunch, they loaded up the wagon and set off.

*Lunch at Toad Hall*

It was a golden afternoon. The smell of the dust they kicked up was rich and satisfying. Out of thick orchards on either side the road, birds whistled to them cheerily. Travelers called out "Good day," or stopped to say nice things about the beautiful wagon.

"Ah," said Toad, kicking out his legs. "This is the real life for a gentleman!"

They had a pleasant journey along the narrow roads. It was not until the afternoon that they reached the highway. There, disaster sprang out on them.

*Toad, Mole, and Rat set off in the wagon.*

They were strolling along the highway when they saw a small cloud of dust. It seemed to be coming at them fast. From out the dust they heard a faint "toot-toot!" that sounded like an animal in pain. They turned to continue talking. But in an instant, everything changed. With a blast of wind and a whirl of sound that made them jump for the nearest ditch, it was on them!

The horn of the motor car rang out, "TOOT-TOOT!" They had a quick look at an interior of glittering glass and leather. Then, the magnificent motor car flung a cloud of dust that blinded them and dwindled to a speck in the distance.

The old grey horse and the wagon lurched forward. Then, there was an awful crash. The yellow-colored wagon, their beautiful wagon, fell over onto its side in the ditch.

Rat danced up and down in the road.

"You villains!" he shouted, shaking both fists. "You scoundrels! You, you, road hogs! I'll call the police on you! I'll report you!"

*"TOOT-TOOT!" the horn rang out.*

# Chapter 11 The Open Road, Part IV

Where was Toad? He was sitting in the middle of the dusty road and staring in the direction of the disappearing motor car. He went into a sort of a trance. His face looked calm and he murmured, "toot-toot!"

Rat shook him by the shoulder, but Toad did not budge.

"What a beautiful sight!" Toad murmured. "That is the REAL way to travel! The ONLY way to travel! O my! O my! I must get one!"

Mole tapped the Rat on the shoulder, but Toad went on.

"To think I never KNEW!" he said. "All those wasted years that lie behind me. I never knew. I never even dreamed of it! But NOW—now that I know—oh, what fun awaits me! What dust clouds shall form behind me as I speed on my way! What wagons I shall fling carelessly into the ditch! Those awful little wagons, common wagons, yellow-colored wagons!"

"What should we do with him?" asked Mole

Toad murmured, *"toot-toot!"*

"There is nothing to be done," said Rat. "He is mad. He has got a new craze. It is always like this, in the first stage. He'll go on like that for days now, walking in a happy dream, not able to do anything useful. Never mind him. Let's go and see what can be done about the wagon."

They inspected the wagon and found that it would no longer travel. One wheel had been broken into bits.

"Come on!" said the Rat. "We'll have to walk. It's five or six miles to the nearest town. The sooner we get started the better."

"But what about Toad?" asked Mole. "We can't leave him here, sitting in the middle of the road by himself! It's not safe. What if another ... thing ... were to come along?'

"Never mind him," said Rat. "I'm done with him!"

*Rat and Mole inspected the wagon.*

They had not gone very far, however, when there were footsteps behind them. Toad caught up with them and put a paw inside the elbow of each of them.

"Now, look here Toad!" said Rat sharply. "As soon as we get to the town, you'll have to go straight to the police station. You must see if they know anything about that motor car. You must find out who it belongs to. You must complain because your wagon is broken. Then, you'll have to go to a blacksmith so he can fix the wagon. Meanwhile, Mole and I will find rooms where we can stay until the wagon is ready."

"Police station? Complain?" murmured Toad dreamily. "Why on earth would I complain about that beautiful motor car? I am done with wagons forever. I never want to see the wagon again or hear of it. O, Ratty!"

*Toad caught up with Rat and Mole.*

The animals spent the night. The next day, Rat and Mole made their way back to the river bank.

A few days later, Mole was sitting on the bank fishing, when Rat strolled up.

"Have you heard the news?" Rat asked. "Everyone's talking about it. Toad went to town on the train this morning. He has ordered a large and very expensive motor car."

*Rat told Mole the news.*

# CORE KNOWLEDGE LANGUAGE ARTS

## SERIES EDITOR-IN-CHIEF
E. D. Hirsch, Jr.

## PRESIDENT
Linda Bevilacqua

### EDITORIAL STAFF
Carolyn Gosse, Senior Editor - Preschool
Khara Turnbull, Materials Development Manager
Michelle L. Warner, Senior Editor - Listening & Learning

Mick Anderson
Robin Blackshire
Maggie Buchanan
Paula Coyner
Sue Fulton
Sara Hunt
Erin Kist
Robin Luecke
Rosie McCormick
Cynthia Peng
Liz Pettit
Ellen Sadler
Deborah Samley
Diane Auger Smith
Sarah Zelinke

### DESIGN AND GRAPHICS STAFF
Scott Ritchie, Creative Director

Kim Berrall
Michael Donegan
Liza Greene
Matt Leech
Bridget Moriarty
Lauren Pack

### CONSULTING PROJECT MANAGEMENT SERVICES
ScribeConcepts.com

### ADDITIONAL CONSULTING SERVICES
Ang Blanchette
Dorrit Green
Carolyn Pinkerton

## ACKNOWLEDGMENTS

These materials are the result of the work, advice, and encouragement of numerous individuals over many years. Some of those singled out here already know the depth of our gratitude; others may be surprised to find themselves thanked publicly for help they gave quietly and generously for the sake of the enterprise alone. To helpers named and unnamed we are deeply grateful.

### CONTRIBUTORS TO EARLIER VERSIONS OF THESE MATERIALS

Susan B. Albaugh, Kazuko Ashizawa, Nancy Braier, Kathryn M. Cummings, Michelle De Groot, Diana Espinal, Mary E. Forbes, Michael L. Ford, Ted Hirsch, Danielle Knecht, James K. Lee, Diane Henry Leipzig, Martha G. Mack, Liana Mahoney, Isabel McLean, Steve Morrison, Juliane K. Munson, Elizabeth B. Rasmussen, Laura Tortorelli, Rachael L. Shaw, Sivan B. Sherman, Miriam E. Vidaver, Catherine S. Whittington, Jeannette A. Williams

We would like to extend special recognition to Program Directors Matthew Davis and Souzanne Wright who were instrumental to the early development of this program.

### SCHOOLS

We are truly grateful to the teachers, students, and administrators of the following schools for their willingness to field test these materials and for their invaluable advice: Capitol View Elementary, Challenge Foundation Academy (IN), Community Academy Public Charter School, Lake Lure Classical Academy, Lepanto Elementary School, New Holland Core Knowledge Academy, Paramount School of Excellence, Pioneer Challenge Foundation Academy, New York City PS 26R (The Carteret School), PS 30X (Wilton School), PS 50X (Clara Barton School), PS 96Q, PS 102X (Joseph O. Loretan), PS 104Q (The Bays Water), PS 214K (Michael Friedsam), PS 223Q (Lyndon B. Johnson School), PS 308K (Clara Cardwell), PS 333Q (Goldie Maple Academy), Sequoyah Elementary School, South Shore Charter Public School, Spartanburg Charter School, Steed Elementary School, Thomas Jefferson Classical Academy, Three Oaks Elementary, West Manor Elementary.

And a special thanks to the CKLA Pilot Coordinators Anita Henderson, Yasmin Lugo-Hernandez, and Susan Smith, whose suggestions and day-to-day support to teachers using these materials in their classrooms was critical.